-Applying-

THE 7 LAWS OF SPRITUAL SUCCESS

-Applying-

THE 7 LAWS OF SPIRITUAL SUCCESS

The workbook to accompany
THE 7 LAWS OF SPIRITUAL SUCCESS
by Selwyn Hughes

Jennifer Oldroyd

CONTENTS

FOREWORD

'No matter how powerful and effective the ointment,' said an ancient philosopher, 'it is of little use unless it is applied to the affected part.' It is the same with truth; its power lies not just in the insight it brings but also in its application.

Application is the theme of this workbook and study guide written by Jennifer Oldroyd. She has set out to help you relate the concepts contained in *The 7 Laws of Spiritual Success* to your daily spiritual life and experience. You will see also that she has brought some further insights into the topics discussed which will help expand your understanding of these important biblical concepts.

I wish to record my thanks and appreciation for the time and effort she has put into making *The 7 Laws of Spiritual Success* more readily accessible for those who wish to pursue them either as a personal study or in company with others at a homegroup, a weekend retreat, a coffee morning and so on.

The key to getting the best out of this study guide is to begin by reading through the Preface. This provides you with recommendations on how to use this book. I can't stress enough how important it is to do this.

My prayer is that this study guide will not only clarify the concepts contained in *The 7 Laws of Spiritual Success*, but will help you to apply them to your life in a way that will deepen your walk with the Lord and enable you to become an even bigger and better channel through whom Christ's love can flow to others.

My love in the Lord Jesus

Selwyn Hughes

PREFACE

This workbook has been produced to help you make the most of *The 7 Laws of Spiritual Success*. Selwyn Hughes has distilled 50 years of teaching and ministry into what he believes is an irreducible minimum of just seven elements. To spend time studying these elements will be like a spiritual health check. It will enable you to measure your priorities and your heart condition, and to make a diagnosis with the help of the Holy Spirit.

You would consult a doctor about symptoms that trouble you, or a nutritionist about problems with your weight, or an optician about failing eyesight. What do you do when spiritual problems confront you? When prayer is difficult, worship feels dull and lifeless, when the Scriptures themselves are dry and unappetising?

One thing you can do is to turn back the pages of your Christian experience, and look once again at those basic premises which once seemed so life-changing. Maybe you have become unforgiving to someone. Maybe you have lost the habit of gratitude to God for His many blessings. Maybe you have given up trying so hard.

As you open your mind and heart to these first principles, it may be that you will need to make some changes; to repent and turn from some wrong attitudes. The probing questions and practical Action Plan in each chapter will help you do just that.

HOW TO USE THIS BOOK

1. You will need to have read right through *The 7 Laws of Spiritual Success* at least once, but preferably twice.

2. Decide how much time you want to spend on each chapter. If you are studying alone, you may want to do, say, 15 minutes a day, taking one section at a time. If you are studying as a group, then you might want to spend one or two sessions on each chapter.

3. Each section of the workbook contains questions to help you think through and apply what you have learned. Space has been left on the pages for you to note down answers to the questions, but a separate notebook would enable you to make more extensive notes, including prayers, thoughts and specific courses of action. The more practical your response, the more you are likely to see God at work in your life.

4. At the end of each chapter you will find an Action Plan. This consists of suggestions, questions and ideas for putting into practice the lessons learned. Even if you are using this book for personal and private study, it would be good to share this section with one or two others. Agreeing together on specific courses of action will strengthen your resolve, empower your prayers and offer a better chance of

actually making changes in your life and the life of your church.

5. Selwyn Hughes is an experienced counsellor and an inspiring writer, but his aim is to direct your thoughts and attention to Scripture. Refer constantly to your Bible throughout. Check all the references, and read the verses before and after the selected portions. And each time you begin to study, ask the Holy Spirit to guide, challenge and inspire you.

Most courses of study finish with an examination to discover what you have learned and how well you understand it. Here you will find no such test. There are plenty of questions, but no 'right' answers. The exam you will take will be the daily one of living out the purposes of God, making His kingdom come and His will done in your sphere of life. You will receive no diploma, but if you truly try to live your life according to the laws of God, you will one day receive a crown, and hear His voice saying, 'Well done, good and faithful servant!'

Introduction:

'You'd Better Change Course'

"A book that helped me more than any other was Professor Henry Drummond's Natural Law in the Spiritual World *... as I sought to understand the concept of laws being present not only in the natural world but also in the spiritual world ...*

As I pondered this issue I tried to imagine a universe where everything happened not by law but by chance ... " (p.3)

NATURAL LAWS

The first chapter of Genesis introduces us to the Creator God. A child reading this account of the beginning of our world might say, 'God made the sun. God made the birds. God made the flowers. God made me.' The child would be right, but would only have brushed the surface of what Genesis is telling us about the Creator.

Dig a little deeper into those verses and you will find that what God was doing was not only bringing the physical world into being, but also anchoring it to His will with immutable laws. Not only did He say, 'Let there be light', He also decided how fast it would travel, and established the laws of reflection and refraction. Not only did He create the sun and the stars, He also established their orbits, and the rhythm that governs our lives: the mornings and evenings, the days and the weeks, the months and the years.

And this is the same God who rules over the spiritual realm.

Those who are art critics can often name the artist of any painting instantly. They recognise the brush work, the use of light and shade, the way in which paint is applied. In the same way, we can recognise the hand of God. *'The great lines running through the universe which we call "laws" do not stop at what scientists call "the natural sphere", but are to be observed in the spiritual sphere also'* (p.2). In the pages that follow, Selwyn Hughes demonstrates that there are laws which govern the spiritual world, recognising in their design and immutability the same Artist who created the wonderful universe in which we live.

Questions to consider

- 'The idea was quite new to me' (p.2). Is this idea new to you? What is your initial response?

• Selwyn Hughes' guest was 'a young scientist' (p.2). Do you think that might have coloured the way he thought?

SPIRITUAL LAWS

When men and women make laws, they often have to change them in order to reflect the changes in society. For example, in Britain the licensing laws have changed, and lots of pubs and bars now stay open all day. And it is no longer against the law to have a homosexual relationship.

This happens in the Church also. The Anglican Church has changed the law on women in the priesthood. And they are considering changing the law on remarriage of divorced persons.

For us, laws are tools that we use to govern society, to make our citizens feel safe and protected, and to provide a pattern for living that will be the best for the majority. And when we think the tool has become 'outdated', we scrap it.

However, in this next section of his Introduction, Selwyn Hughes introduces the idea that the spiritual laws which the Creator God has established are '*as sure, certain and reliable as those we have discovered in the natural realm'* (p.4). This is the idea that we are going to have to accept before we go any further in this book. If it is true, then the principles of worship, forgiveness, perseverance, and so on, are not optional extras. They are not laws that operated in the eighteenth or nineteenth or twentieth century, but not in the twenty-first. 'Obey and you get results; disobey and you get consequences' (p.9). This is as true for us as it was for Adam.

Questions to consider

- Does the thought of immutable spiritual laws make you feel secure, or threatened? (See the lighthouse story on p.11!)

- *'It is impossible for us to break laws; we only break ourselves upon them'* (Cecil B. DeMille, p.11). Have you ever experienced this? What happened?

TRUE SUCCESS

What did you think when you first saw the title of this book?
There are probably Christians who would be offended by each
part of the title. Only *seven* laws? But we are not under *law* any
more! And, of course, surely it's wrong to talk of spiritual *success*?

The dictionary gives a number of definitions of the word
success: 'good fortune; prosperous progress or achievement; the
attainment of wealth, influence or acclaim'. As those who want
to follow the carpenter of Nazareth, we would want to repudiate
some of these concepts.

But, as Selwyn Hughes shows, the idea of progress or
achievement is not an unbiblical one and nor, actually, is the
idea of prosperity – not the prosperity of 'wealth, influence or
acclaim', but that of 'soul prosperity' (p.13).

> *Does the Bible use the concept of success? Most definitely.*
> *The word 'success' and its synonyms, appears many times in*
> *Scripture. Here are just a few:*
>
> > *Do not let this Book of the Law depart from your mouth;*
> > *meditate on it day and night, so that you may be careful*
> > *to do everything written in it. Then you will be*

prosperous and successful.

Josh. 1:8

He [Uzziah] sought God during the days of Zechariah, who instructed him in the fear of God. As long as he sought the LORD, God gave him success.

2 Chron. 26:5

So he sent David away from him and gave him command over a thousand men, and David led the troops in their campaigns. In everything he did he had great success, because the LORD was with him.

1 Sam. 18:13–14

What did God have in mind when He said He would give His servants success? It meant of course that God would bless the work of their hands, but God had in mind soul prosperity, too. (p.13)

If we are honest, we do want to make progress with God. We want to learn more about Him, to understand more of His Word, to serve Him better. That, for us, would be success. If we want success in the garden, the farm or the laboratory, we have to work within the natural laws. And if we want success in the spiritual life, then we have to recognise the laws that operate there too.

Questions to consider

- *'Success in a Christian sense is this: knowing the will of God and doing it'* (p.14). On this basis, would you say you are making a success of your spiritual life?

- *'No one can be truly successful if he or she is not a person of character'* (p.14). Who is the most spiritually 'successful' person you know? Does his or her life and character bear this statement out?

ACTION PLAN

- *'The law of the Spirit of life, the controlling power of the Holy Spirit – who is life-giving – is stronger in the believer than the controlling power of sin which ultimately produces death'* (p.5). Spend some time asking the Holy Spirit to use the study of this book to lead you into the truth.

- Look up the word 'success' in a concordance, and note how often in Scripture God promises it, and grants it, to those who are truly searching for Him and trying to obey Him.

- Make a list of the areas of your Christian life that you feel are the weakest, and ask God to use this book to reveal where you are going wrong. Keep a record of the answers!

- Selwyn Hughes used the concept of spiritual laws in this book in his work as a pastor and counsellor. Think about what areas of your life it could impact: your job, raising your children, teaching Sunday school, caring for elderly relatives, and so on.

- Ask God to plant the principle of this book in your mind as an *'"apperception thought" … a powerful notion or idea that establishes itself in your mind and around which other similar ideas and thoughts easily encrust'* (p.6), and to speak to you in lots of different ways as you work through the study.

Law 1

First
Things
First

"The first responsibility of every Christian is to worship God. It is, I believe, the first law of the soul. *When we violate that law we put our souls in peril "* (p.21)

MAKE WORSHIP YOUR FIRST FOCUS

In recent years there has been a spate of TV programmes and newspaper articles devoted to 'lists': the top 100 people, or books, or programmes. Even if we find our personal favourite down at number 75, we still want to know what made 'Number One'.

As you start this journey with Selwyn Hughes, this spiritual check-up, are you surprised by his 'Number One'? What did you think it would be? What would you have voted for? What one element of the Christian faith and journey would *you* have put at the top?

Selwyn Hughes has drawn on his experiences in churches, fellowships and in the counselling room, to highlight that when we fail to put the worship of God first in our hearts and minds, in our thinking and planning, in our work and witness, we fail to become what God created us to be.

Many organisations now require their employees to keep a record of how they spend their time at work. Our perception of what we do all day can often differ greatly from the reality. Making a note of every action and how long it took can soon throw up answers to the question, 'Where did the time go?'

So, too, for us as Christians. We may think that we give generously – but do we keep a careful record? We may think that we are living a life of prayer – but how much time is actually spent in prayer? And we may believe that the worship of God is a clear priority, but even a quick 'stock take' may reveal that this is not so. We may indeed spend time on Sunday worshipping God with our friends and family, but as Selwyn Hughes says:

> … *it is not so much with corporate worship I am concerned here; rather it is with individual worship. I am thinking of it in the way that Jesus used the word when tempted by the devil in the wilderness. (p.20)*

Questions to consider

• Is the worship of God a missing element in your life, or in the life of your church (p.18)?

- On p.23 Selwyn says, '*God meant that every convert should learn first how to worship Him and only after that become a worker.*' Was that your experience as a new Christian? How were you taught about worship?

- Read Genesis 22:1–14 and Job 1. How do these stories change your view of what worship is?

WORSHIP AND OUR UNDERSTANDING OF GOD

Sunday schools are a rich source of funny stories about children's misunderstandings. There was the child who thought the song said that God would make us 'vicious old men', rather than 'fishers of men'. Or the little boy who prayed, 'Our Father, who art in heaven, Harold be thy name ...'

Inexperience and immaturity may result in misunderstanding. If not sorted out, misunderstanding may lead to wrong beliefs, and wrong beliefs may lead to all kinds of problems in our emotional and spiritual lives.

On pages 28–35, Selwyn Hughes explores some of these problems, and shows the importance of trusting God, and also having a true and right concept of God.

If you are a self-taught tennis player or golfer, you may have had to resort to proper instruction to take you forward in your game. And you may have found that some bad techniques have had to be 'unlearned'. Similarly, whether you have been a Christian a long time, or just a few years, there may be some ideas and beliefs that you have absorbed that will have to be discarded.

On page 32 is the story of Dr Joseph Cooke, who '*invented an impossible God*'. It may be that your own background and upbringing have left you with an understanding of God that is false. Your parents' beliefs, your experiences as a child or young person, unhappy situations with other Christians – these may all have shaped your view of God. And, as Selwyn Hughes explains, it is your view of God that determines your worship.

The good news, however, is that the work of the Holy Spirit is to lead us into all truth (John 16:13). Ask Him to show you whether there is any misunderstanding or wrong view of God in your life, and to teach you how to worship in spirit and in truth.

Questions to consider

- Has anything happened in your life that has made it difficult for you to trust God (p.30)?

- How do you feel about the quote from *The Lion, the Witch and the Wardrobe* on page 33 about God not being 'safe'?

WORSHIP AND WORK

Every time a sermon is given on the story of Mary and Martha, there will be some dear lady in the congregation who will go out of church muttering, 'That's all very well, but *someone* has to cook the dinner.'

The Protestant work ethic is alive and well and living in many Christian homes and workplaces and churches. The busier we are, the more we think we are serving God and pleasing Him. Meetings and committees, youth work and evangelism, services and celebrations, catering and counselling – we fill our time with the things we do for God. The thought of Mary, sitting smugly and comfortably at Jesus' feet, secretly annoys us, and if we end up burnt out and close to a nervous breakdown, we see it as an acceptable sacrifice to God.

This last section of Selwyn Hughes' chapter underlines for us that those who serve best are actually those who serve as a consequence of their worship of God.

So what does that mean in practice? Must I join a contemplative order? Must I rise at 5am every day to worship God before I do anything else? Must I give up all my 'Christian work' until I've got the balance right?

Selwyn Hughes suggests reading Matthew 1:28–29 in *The Message*, and meditating on that lovely phrase 'the rhythms of grace'. The whole created world has a rhythm: day and night, work and rest, times of growth and times of dormancy. By putting the worship of God first in our lives, we will more easily 'find the rhythm'.

Questions to consider

- Oswald Chambers says, '*The biggest competitor for devotion is service*' (p.37). Do you think that Christian work has a right place in your life, or has it become a greater priority than worship?

- Do you identify with the quote from Eugene Peterson on page 38: '*Without worship we live manipulated and manipulating lives*'? Do you feel that events in your life have 'manipulated' you?

ACTION PLAN

- *'We hardly know where to begin because we have lost nearly all contact with the past'* (Robert Webber, p.19). Write down now some ideas of how you could begin to give the worship of God its rightful place in your life and the life of your church.

- *'One of the failures of modern-day Christians is to put work before worship. We take our converts and immediately set about making workers out of them. God never meant it to be so'* (p.23). What plans could your church make to ensure that new Christians are taught correctly about the primacy of worship?

- *'Most problems arise in the personality as a result of our failure truly to worship God'* (Larry Crabb, p.29). Are there problems in your life or in the life of your church? Start to look at those problems in the light of this chapter: how might your problems be connected with your attitude to the worship of God? How can you begin to change things?

- *'I urge you, before you go any further, to think through this issue of how you see God, for if you do not see Him as He really is – trustworthy, reliable and good – then those doubts and misgivings will sabotage true worship'* (p.33). Sit down with another person and take it in turns to describe God to each other. What are the words and phrases you each use, and what do they tell you about your perception of God? How might you develop your view of God?

- *'When I meet a Christian leader I meet a manager'* (Os Guinness, p.37). How can your church encourage its leaders to get the balance right between work and worship?

Law 2

Count Your Blessings

"*It is another law of life, I believe, that the more we dwell on what we have, rather than what we don't have, the more the personality is drawn to health* " (p.42)

FOCUS ON YOUR BLESSINGS

The first story in this chapter is about someone who regularly, first thing in the morning, lists five new things that God has done for him. But have you ever noticed how easy it is to build up a list of negative things?

It may be that some really bad thing happens to us. Perhaps redundancy, or cancer, or bereavement. We start to learn to deal with it. But then something else happens. Something much smaller, but still bad – maybe a back problem, or a financial setback. Somehow, it seems that our human nature desires to demonstrate to the world how badly we have been treated. So we add the two things together. First the death, and then the bad back. After that, it is only too easy to add to the list every single negative thing that takes place in life.

Selwyn Hughes as a counsellor has wide experience of the kind of depression, inward-looking mentality and spiritual disease that is caused by this kind of 'adding up'.

The path to spiritual health is through ensuring that our mental list is one of blessings and good things, rather than setbacks and bad things.

Questions to consider

- Is your personality one that is naturally drawn to positive thoughts, or do you find the lesson in this chapter hard to learn?

- The man in the story on pages 43–45 had his perspective changed by seeing others much worse off than himself. Would that work for you?

- What one thing, more than any other, makes your heart well up in gratitude to God?

THE ATTITUDE OF GRATITUDE

Are you a natural 'thank-er'? Do you always send a thank you note after a meal out? Do you write thank you letters after Christmas? Have you ever sent letters such as those described on page 47 – notes of appreciation to those who have helped you or encouraged you in life?

There is no doubt that depression and misery make us inward looking. And when we get into that state it is very difficult to think of others and to imagine how they feel. It is difficult, too, to turn our hearts in gratitude and thankfulness to our heavenly Father for all His blessings and goodness to us.

Imagine a small boy. It is about eight weeks before Christmas. The boy wants a bicycle for Christmas, and he begins to drop hints. 'I *really* would like a bike. All my friends have got one. Dad, you used to have a bike when you were young. Why can't I have one?'

And so it goes on, week after week, until Christmas morning arrives. There, at the end of the bed, is a shiny new bicycle – just what he wanted. Does the boy say, 'Well, what a coincidence! I was hoping for a bike!' No! He runs into his parents' room and throws himself into their arms. 'Thank you! Thank you! It's wonderful!'

The difference between the two lies in the relationship between the boy and his father. He knows that his request has been heard, that his father loves him and has chosen the best for him. And so he runs to offer his thanks. (And his father will probably ensure that he sits down and writes thank you letters for all his other Christmas presents, too!)

Questions to consider

• How often do you take time to '*notice the hand of God*' in your life (Charles Spurgeon, p.46)? Is thankfulness a part of your daily prayer time?

• '*The Almighty often sends His special blessings by way of people and I think He likes His agents to be thanked also*' (p.48). Do you regularly thank the people who bring God's blessings into your life?

CHOOSE TO BE THANKFUL

It is often the case that those Christians who have grown up in the Roman Catholic Church, or in the higher churches of the Anglican communion, understand much better the necessity for living by the will, rather than by feelings.

As Selwyn Hughes says on page 51, people will sometimes label as hypocrisy the offering of worship or prayer when we don't 'feel like it'.

In his book *A Long Obedience in the Same Direction* (IVP), Eugene Peterson says:

We can act ourselves into a new way of feeling much quicker than we can feel ourselves into a new way of acting. Worship is an act that develops feelings for God, not a feeling for God that is expressed in worship.

So, you are having a bad day. Lots of small problems. Your plans didn't work out. The sun didn't shine. Your feelings have taken a slide. You look, act and feel grumpy. What are you going to do?

Are you going to compose a negative list, and reel if off to your family on your return home? Or are you going to do as the psalmist did in Psalm 103, and charge your soul to praise the Lord? '*He is saying, in effect, I am going to use my will to stir up my mind to focus on reasons why I should praise the Lord. I may not feel like doing it but I am going to do it anyway!*' (p.51).

Scripture is full of incidences when the people of God were reminded of God's blessings. How many times, I wonder, does the phrase 'who brought you out of Egypt' occur? A wonderful, stupendous act of God, which resulted in freedom and the beginning of a new life. What better way to deal with grumpiness than to remember something fantastic?

Questions to consider

- Is there an incident in your life that just thinking about makes you feel better? Perhaps your conversion, or a miracle of healing?

- *'You can trace every good and perfect gift to the Father above'* (p.55). Are there good things in your life that you have never really thanked God for?

_____

_____

_____

_____

GIVING THANKS IN EVERYTHING

Many years ago, a book was published in this country which divided Christians into two camps. Merlin Carothers' *Prison to Praise* was an impassioned plea to the people of God to praise Him in everything. But some people found it impossible to praise God for cancer, or road accidents, or disaster. They could trust God for His help, and thank Him for it, but they could not praise Him for the problem itself. That felt like blasphemy.

Take a few moments to re-read the story of Corrie ten Boom on page 60. Then remind yourself of the story of Joseph in Genesis chapters 37–45. Standing outside the situation, we can see the hand of God. From inside, it's a different story.

There may be something in your life right now that seems to you to be anything but a blessing. But *'No matter what happens to you God is committed to working good out of it and because of that it is possible to thank Him for everything that happens to you'* (p.59). Our belief in the goodness of God may begin with His mercies to us in conversion and provision, but it will grow as we see Him at work in the disasters and the problems. Just think: every Sunday you join with others in thanking God that His Son, Jesus Christ, suffered a horrible death. Why? Because you know the stupendous things that death achieved in the purposes of God. *'If you start there then I promise you it won't be long before you begin to develop a right response to all the setbacks of life. You will find yourself saying, even in the most difficult of circumstances, 'Thank you, Lord, for letting this happen. I can't wait to see how You are going to turn it to good'* (p.59).

Questions to consider

• Is there something in your life that you find it difficult to thank God for? Can you imagine how it might turn out in a way that would demonstrate His love and concern for you?

- How would you help someone who is going through a difficult time, and who felt that God was far away?

ACTION PLAN

- '*You might be better off adopting Sir John Templeton's approach by lying quietly in your bed after you have awakened and thinking of five new ways you have been blessed*' (p.42). Keep a notebook by your bed, and use it to record the good things that God gives you.

- '*I think He likes His agents to be thanked*' (p.48). Think of three people who have been influential in your life, and write letters of thanks to them.

- '*It's sad when Christians wait until they feel like praising rather than using their wills to command their minds to focus on reasons for praise*' (p.52). Plan into your prayers definite times when you thank God for the *common* blessings, the *special* blessings, and the *spiritual* blessings He has given you (p.54).

- *'The world is flooded with bad news'* (p.45). How might your church ensure that prayer times have a right balance between thanksgiving and supplication?

- *'We forget the good things God has done for us'* (p.53). In your family, plan regular times to think back and remember God's blessings. Use photograph albums, family videos and other reminders of happy times.

Law 3

Keep On
Keeping On

"It is a law of the soul that those who keep on keeping on and never give up will find their souls fortified for the task. They will not only find a reward waiting them at the end but they will experience the blessing of God on the way to that reward" (p.68)

PERSEVERANCE

Have you noticed how hard it is these days to find people prepared to take on long-term commitments? It has become almost impossible to find leaders for the uniformed youth movements like Scouts and Guides. It is difficult to find people prepared to take on a Sunday school class or to help with church cleaning. Why is this?

You will find a clue to the answer if you spend any time watching television. In the soap operas, for example, listen out for the words, 'It's not working out, is it?' Marriages are dissolved, partnerships brought to an end, relationships die, jobs are thrown up. The moment difficulties arise, the answer is to get out. If at first you don't succeed – give up. That's the motto of the culture we live in.

But in this chapter, Selwyn Hughes draws us away from the world's attitudes, and fixes our attention on the Scriptures, and the need for perseverance. As the quote from John Stott says, '*We must resist the intellectual and moral pressure of our contemporary world and refuse to conform to the fashions of the day*' (p.69).

Spend a few moments looking up the references quoted on pages 68–69. Then take a look at the letters to the churches in Revelation 2 and 3, with their exhortations to faithfulness and perseverance, and their promises to those who 'overcome'. Soak your mind in these verses and pray that God will give you the strength to persevere.

Questions to consider

- Looking at the story of Winston Churchill (pp.66–67), how would you define the difference between stubbornness and perseverance?

- How would you describe your own record of perseverance? Are you a stay-er, or do you quickly give up on things and move on?

THE REASONS PEOPLE GIVE UP

Selwyn Hughes, with his great experience in counselling, has talked with and helped many people with their problems, and he is therefore not afraid to look those problems in the face and to tackle them in the light of Scripture and the promises of God.

Unfortunately, the preacher Selwyn Hughes quotes on page 71 is not unique. There are still those who assure their congregations that good health and prosperity are our right as children of God and inhabitants of the kingdom of heaven. However, as Selwyn Hughes reminds us, Jesus in John 16:33 says differently: '*In this world you will have trouble ...*'

> *Why do people fail to be steadfast and persevere? Why do they defect? This is an issue that has exercised me greatly over the years. My research into this subject has revealed that in the*

main those who fall by the way do so for four reasons.

1. They become discouraged by reason of trials and troubles.

2. They are unable to deal with doubts about the faith.

3. They are overcome by persecution from others.

4. They fall into sin and do not know how to rise again.

(p.70)

The following questions look at these four main reasons why believers fail to persevere in the faith. Together with another Christian, spend a few minutes asking the Holy Spirit to help you work through these, and to bring into the light any areas of weakness or potential failure. Then pray for one another, that God will provide you with '*the inner strength to persevere and overcome every obstacle that confronts [you]*' (p.72).

Questions to consider

- Trials and trouble
  '*Life is more tragic than orderly*' (Oswald Chambers, p.70).
  Have you experienced tragedy in your life? How did it affect your belief and faith in God?

- *'Life is not just something to be enjoyed but rather is a task that each one of us is assigned'* (p.71). Do you believe this? Do you see problems as 'tasks' from God, or as interruptions to your fellowship with Him?

- *'Unmerited suffering is a problem for many'* (p.71). Imagine the young woman whose children died (p.71). is in your church. How would you go about helping her?

- Doubts about the faith
  What aspects of Christian belief have you ever had doubts about? How did you deal with your doubts?

....

....

....

- '*Satan is a tempter. The art of doubting is natural to us in our fallen condition, but Satan often works on our doubts and tempts us to unbelief* (p.74). Have you blamed yourself for your slide into unbelief? Can you see how your doubts might have been worked on by Satan?

....

....

....

- Persecution
Have you experienced hostility or mockery for your faith? How did you deal with it?

....

....

....

....

- When you fall into sin
  Have you ever been so ashamed of something you have done, that you were ready to give up the Christian life (p.80)? How did you deal with that?

  _____

  _____

  _____

  _____

- *'The real problem was the lack of firm moral resolve'* (p.81). How can you strengthen your moral resolve so that you can avoid sin?

  _____

  _____

  _____

  _____

RUN THE FULL RACE

There is all the difference in the world between the amateur and the professional. St Paul's three examples to Timothy in 2 Timothy 2 – the soldier, the athlete and the farmer – show up that difference most dramatically. Training, discipline and more discipline are what make a soldier, not a uniform. Training, discipline and more training, are what make an athlete successful, not the latest sportswear. Experience, hard work and more hard work are what bring the farmer's rewards, not a new tractor.

It's the long haul that is important. We need to know where we are going to draw our strength from in the long term. Today's church meeting may have been inspiring and encouraging, but the glow will fade, and reality will be there when we wake tomorrow morning.

> *Packer suggests that the secret of recovering your spiritual footing at a time when everything is falling around you lies in the little word 'think'.*
>
> *Doubtless David would have focused his mind on God. And that is the secret we must learn, to keep our minds on Him – His greatness, His power and, above all, His ability to bring good out of everything.* (p.85)

Questions to consider

- *'I'm giving it everything I've got'* (1 Cor. 9:26, *The Message*; p.83). Can you honestly say that you are giving the Christian life 'everything you've got'?

....

....

....

- On page 85, Selwyn Hughes imagines how David might have gone about finding strength in God. What helps and encourages you to persevere?

....

....

....

ACTION PLAN

- *'Never give up'* (p.67).
  Is there an area of your life where you are conscious of having 'given up'? What one thing could you do to begin to put things right?

- *'The soul will not flourish simply by going to church, singing a few hymns and thinking your Christian duty has been done'* (p.69).

How good is your church at encouraging members in their daily lives? How might support be offered to those going through difficult times?

* *'So many Christians complain of spiritual doubt while all the time they do not use the secret weapon'* (p.76).
  How much do you read the Bible? Be honest! What could you do to increase your knowledge of God's Word?

* *'He … centred his thoughts on the promises that God had made to him'* (Jim Packer, p.85).
  Is there a promise of God that is very special to you? How can you use that to help you persevere in difficult times?

* *'Don't give up. If God has called you to do something then make sure you finish it. Struggle is the chrysalis out of which a new vision of God comes. When pressure comes against you, persevere. God will not let you down. You will find that His strength is more than a match for anything you are called to face'* (p.86).
  Make a list of the things you do for God: your job, caring for your family, teaching in Sunday school, and so on. Then write down

    (a) what might cause to you give up on that task; and

    (b) how you can find the strength to persevere.

Law 4

Remember to Forget

"It is another law of life, I believe, that spiritual health and success depend on our ability to forget the hurts and injuries that others have given us – not to have them erased from memory, but to deal with them in such a way that we are not emotionally overwhelmed by them." (p.91)

THE POWER TO FORGET

*P*recious though a good memory is, the power to forget is equally precious. Henri Gergson, the French philosopher, said, 'It is the function of the brain to enable us not only to remember but also to forget.'

Much of the time I have spent in helping people with their problems over the years has been focused on helping people forget. This is because so often when I have encouraged people to let go of the past with all its hurts and painful memories and to forgive those who have hurt them they have responded by saying, 'I can forgive but I can't forget.' They forgive but they don't want the other person to forget they have forgiven (p.89).

Sometimes, when people are involved in road accidents, they find that the last few seconds before the impact, and the moment of the accident itself, are a complete blank. The brain has 'edited out' something too painful and traumatic to remember.

Others, however, remember in startling detail all the circumstances that led up to the incident, and they play it over and over again in their waking and sleeping moments. They are haunted by the trauma for weeks or months afterwards.

We have no control over such responses. We either live with the blank in our minds; or we learn to cope with the memories. But we can't decide which.

In this chapter, Selwyn Hughes makes it absolutely clear that in our Christian lives, we *do* have a choice. We have to decide whether we will we allow the mercy of God to help us forget injury and hurt, or go over and over it in our minds, keeping alive the sense of pain and injustice.

'*One cannot of course forget the facts; it is the bitterness and the emotional overwhelming from which deliverance may be found*' (p.92). That is the key to this chapter. We can't choose to forget an incident or a harsh word or action. It happened, on such-and-such a day, at such-and-such a time. It happened. Nothing will change that. But the pain, the unhappiness, the hurt, the bitterness – those we can be delivered from. Hallelujah!

Questions to consider

- *'I can forgive but I can't forget'* (p.89). Do you sympathise with this response? Have you ever said this?

- Have you ever been *'emotionally overwhelmed'* (p.91) by some hurt or injury – to yourself or someone you love? How did you deal with it?

- *'Forgiveness is a wonderful idea until we have someone to forgive'* (C.S. Lewis, p.95). Why do you think we find forgiveness so hard?

AS YOU HAVE BEEN FORGIVEN

There is one cry, common to all mankind, from Adam in the
Garden of Eden, to the small child growing up in the twenty-
first century: 'It's not fair!' Somehow, deep inside each of us is
the idea that life ought to be just, with goodness rewarded,
wrong punished and virtue recognised and revered.

So when we suffer (as we think) unjustly, or when we are
hurt or injured without having first inflicted hurt ourselves, we
hate the unfairness of it all. 'He started it!' 'Well, you brought the
subject up!' 'It was self-defence, officer!' 'It wasn't my fault!'

But something happens to our values and our ideas when we
become Christians. We move into another dimension, another
kingdom, where goodness goes on being good, even when
crucified. Where peace operates in the middle of a violent storm.
Where love never ends, but goes on and on forgiving wrong.

'*The longest journey in the world, it has been said, is the 18
inches between the head and the heart*' (p.101). And there lies our
problem. We may be well taught in the Christian life, and have
read the story of the unmerciful servant in Matthew 18:21–35
many times, but until our hearts are truly touched by the
amazing fact of God's forgiveness, we won't be freed from that
striving for what the world calls justice.

Questions to consider

- *'When people say to me, "My problem is I can't forgive.' I say, "No, that is not your problem. Your problem is you don't know how much you have been forgiven'* (p.97). How strong is your sense of the forgiveness of God?

- *'At that point Peter got up the nerve to ask, "Master, how many times do I forgive a brother or sister who hurts me? Seven?"... When Jesus replied, "Seven! Hardly! Try seventy times seven ..."* *He is suggesting an infinite number of times'* (p.98–99). Is there a situation in your life where you find it hard to go on forgiving? Why is that?

THE CONSEQUENCES OF NOT FORGIVING

From the story of Adam and Eve onwards, the Scriptures are full of dramatic incidences of people getting their come-uppance. The ground opened and swallowed them up. Or their children were killed. Or the nation was overwhelmed and sent into exile. Even in the New Testament we read how Ananias and Sapphira died as a result of their sin, and Paul writes to the church at Corinth that sin is the reason many have become sick and died.

But such drama is not part of our everyday lives. We discover that a respected church leader has been having an affair for many years. But nothing happens. He may leave the church and set up somewhere else, but no thunderbolts fall on him. His children still flourish. His garden still blooms.

And so we may be led into thinking that the spiritual principle of cause and effect no longer operates. Times have changed. Our culture is more accepting. Everyone is entitled to live the way they choose.

But read again Selwyn Hughes' words on page 106: '*The consequence of not forgiving is deeply serious. I can't tell you the number of people I have met in my time who bore all the marks of having been handed over to the torturers; they had become old before their time, wizened, dried up*'

There really is no doubt about it. The issue of lack of forgiveness is one that carries with it consequences that cannot be avoided. Get down on your knees now, and ask God to help you.

Questions to consider

- *'The sin of unforgiveness ... takes its terrible toll on us* now' (p.104). Do you agree with Selwyn Hughes' interpretation? Have you known bitterness and hate as a result of not being able to forgive someone?

- Do you identify with the testimony of the doctor on page 105? Have you been *'striving unconsciously to pay back the debt'*?

ACTION PLAN

I believe there are three things necessary in order to forgive and forget.

First, focus on how much you have been forgiven. *Think how extensive God's mercy has been in your life. You may think you have committed only little sins but, as someone has put it, there are no little sins, just as there is no little God to sin against ...*

Secondly, deal honestly with any lingering resentments that may be in your soul. *This is always a challenging moment. No doubt some of you reading these lines will have gone through deep hurts and even deep horror. As you think now of that person who hurt you, abused you, slandered or libelled you, tortured you, rejected you, release the poison of bitterness in Jesus' Name. Let it gush out before God and tell Him that you want to be free ...*

Thirdly, ask God to help you forget. *If you accept the responsibility to forgive then God will accept the responsibility to help you forget. You can bank on it. You do the possible, God will do the impossible. It's as simple as that.* (pp.106–109)

- *'Surely you are not sending a Christmas card to* him?' (Sangster, p.88). Is there anyone you have 'crossed off your list' because of some hurt they have done you? Ask God to show you one thing you could do to begin the process of forgiveness and reconciliation.

- *'How many churches split over little issues that ought to be forgotten, instead of being the cause of one group going off in a different direction, fractured, splintered and a monument to failure?'* (p.92). Are there any issues in your church right now which threaten to divide the fellowship? Apply Psalm 119:165 to that situation, and begin to pray daily for peace and reconciliation.

- *'Focus on how much you have been forgiven'* (p.106). Make a list of any sins which you are conscious of, and which you have confessed and asked forgiveness for. Spend some time deliberately thanking God for His grace in forgiving you those things.

- *'Deal honestly with any lingering resentments'* (p.108). Write down the names of any people against whom you feel resentment of any kind. Begin to include a daily prayer for them, and ask God to release you from bitterness against them.

- *'Ask God to help you forget'* (p.109). Find a prayer partner who will pray regularly with you and for you, that God will enable you to 'remember to forget' hurts and injuries in the past.

Law 5

Give Yourself to Others

> *"The law … of being more interested in others than in*
>
> *oneself – is called in Scripture the law of love.*
>
> *The apostle James calls it 'the royal law'* "(p.117)

IMPROVE YOUR SERVE

With the enormous sociological changes in the world in the last hundred years, many of us don't really know what a servant is. The untouchables of India, the cotton-picking slaves of America, the despised scullery maid of Victorian England: these are simply figures in history books.

Companies encourage the lowliest of employees to become shareholders, and so enjoy the right to have a say in the running of the business. In offices and organisations across the world, secretaries are expected to work their way up through the company and become managers in their own right.

The figure wrapped in a towel and washing His friends' feet is totally alien to our culture. And anyway, what does 'foot-washing' mean to ordinary people with family commitments and full-time jobs in the twenty-first century?

Selwyn Hughes directs our thinking first to the very nature of the Trinity, and the relationship between Father, Son and Holy Spirit (p.115). He tells how considering that relationship, and how it is expressed, caused a profound change in his life and ministry.

Pray now that the Holy Spirit will enable you to understand what D. Broughton Knox calls the '*essence of reality*', and how it can change the way in which you think and act.

Questions to consider

- How much do you identify with the experience of Arthur Gordon (p.112)? Has your life so far made you self-centred?

- *If you don't share of yourself in some way or another then you demean yourself. Something within shrivels up and your zest for life will diminish (pp.113–114).*
  Do you agree that without service to others, something within us '*shrivels up*' (p.114). Why do you think that is?

- Have you ever experienced a *'paradigm shift'* (p.114) in your own life? What happened?

THE LAW OF LOVE

The supermarket is crowded with shoppers. Everyone is trying to get through the checkouts as quickly as possible, but one aisle is blocked. A young mother is desperately trying to restrain and quieten a small boy. He is screaming, kicking, throwing himself on the floor and generally letting go in a big way. Some onlookers smile at the mother in sympathy. Others click their tongues in disapproval of her lack of discipline. Most simply shrug their shoulders and remember battles with their own children during the 'terrible twos'.

But what makes small children so prone to tantrums? Is it not that their parents are trying to train them to look away from self, and to consider other people? We come into this world already infected with the *'congenital illness'* of Adam (p.124), and we fight against the instructions to share our toys, to say thank you, to offer the biscuits round first. The story of the little boy and his goldfish on page 125 captures exactly the essence of self-interest that is the hallmark of the human race.

> *Whenever I think of how easily self-interest can arise in our hearts, my mind goes back to a story I heard my father tell. A little boy came home from school one day to discover his pet goldfish lying stiff and motionless on the surface of the goldfish bowl. He was devastated and began to cry.*
>
> *His father tried to console him by saying: 'It's sad when a pet dies, but here's what we will do. We'll put the dead little fish in a matchbox, take it out into the garden and invite your friends to join with us in conducting a funeral service. Then afterwards I will take you and your friends to the ice cream parlour and buy you all an ice cream.'*
>
> *The little boy was cheered by this promise but suddenly he noticed that the goldfish was not dead as he had supposed, but had revived somehow and begun swimming merrily around the bowl. The little boy gave a whoop of joy, and clapped his hands in glee that his pet goldfish was still alive.*
>
> *A few minutes later, however, he remembered the promise of his father to take him and his friends to the ice cream parlour. Now that would no longer be a possibility and he had mixed emotions – gladness that his goldfish was still alive, but sadness that he would miss out on a trip to the ice cream parlour. Eventually one emotion dominated the other and turning to his father said, 'Let's kill it.' (p.125)*

Most of us grow to adulthood with the ability to wear a veneer of politeness and consideration, and our self-interest shows itself only in the 'acceptable' forms of competitiveness, ambition or our keenness to be in authority over others.

Once we become Christians, however, we have to face up to the reality of our own sinfulness and selfishness. Reading the testimonies of Eugene Peterson (p.122) and Selwyn Hughes himself (p.116), we can be encouraged that we are not alone in our battle against self. Others have gone before us, and discovered the spiritual law that if we want to be like Jesus, then we must learn to give ourselves to others in love.

Questions to consider

* What would you say is the main way that self-interest demonstrates itself in your life?

* *'To love is to be vulnerable'* (C.S. Lewis, p.121). Have you been hurt in the past by those you have tried to love? How did you deal with that?

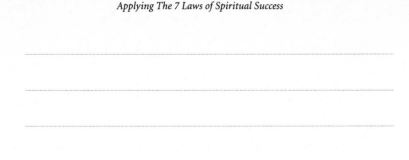

LEARNING TO SERVE

Did you seen the television programme where the life of a large country house in Edwardian times was reconstructed. The house itself was equipped with furnishings, lighting and heating as it would have been, and members of the public were asked to come and play the parts of family, friends and servants.

How revealing it was to eavesdrop on the conversations in the servants' hall, where they battled with their feelings at having to consider the family as their 'betters', and to do the most menial jobs without any thanks. These were people who had chosen to take part, and who, when the programme was over, would go back to their own lives. But still they found it almost impossible to knuckle down and bear the indignity of living as servants.

Spend some time reading through the scriptures on pages 132 and 133, and see how different you are meant to be.

Questions to consider

- *'In a room where nobody saw / And nobody knew'* (p.129).
  Why do you think it is so difficult for us to be loving and
  giving when no one knows about it?

- *'Do nothing out of selfish ambition or vain conceit, but in
  humility consider others better than yourselves. Each of you
  should look not only to your own interests, but also to the
  interests of others. Your attitude should be the same as that of
  Christ Jesus'* (Phil. 2:3–5)
  What do you think it really means to 'consider others better
  than yourselves'?

ACTION PLAN

- *'If one's motives are wrong nothing can be made right'* (Arthur Gordon, p.113).
  List three things that you do (e.g. a job, a church commitment, a family responsibility) and ask God to help you assess the motives you have for doing those things.

- *'One way we can protect ourselves from being hurt is to refuse to be vulnerable, to steel ourselves against other people and stop loving them'* (p.121)
  Is there someone you have stopped loving because of the hurt they have caused you? Before God, decide on one thing you can do to begin to love again.

- *'The Servant King'* (p.126). Deliberately set aside some time to read through St Mark's Gospel. Ask the Holy Spirit to reveal to you Jesus, the Servant King, and how you can follow His example.

- *'Not so with you. Instead, whoever wants to become great among you must be your servant ...'* (Matt. 20:26). How can your church ensure that leaders – house group leaders, worship leaders, youth leaders – understand the principle of servanthood?

- *'Begin to think of ways in which you can minister to others in love'* (p.133). What practical thing might you do in the next few days to begin to bless others and show them God's love?

Tilt your soul in the direction of serving rather than being served, of giving rather than receiving. Develop an attitude of giving. All actions begin with the right attitude. Everyone has their favourite scripture and this is the one, which I quoted before, that I turn to regularly:

Do nothing out of selfish ambition or vain conceit, but in humility consider others better than yourselves. Each of you should look not only to your own interests, but also to the interests of others.

Your attitude should be the same as that of Christ Jesus: Who, being in very nature God,

did not consider equality with God something to be grasped,

but made himself nothing,

taking the very nature of a servant,

being made in human likeness.

Phil. 2:3–7 (pp.133–134)

Law

Stay
Close
to God

6

" Where there is no genuine repentance there can be no ongoing and developing relationship with God. " (p.142)

THE WAY IN

P robably the best illustration of true repentance is still Jesus' story of the Prodigal Son in Luke 15. Selfish, greedy, impatient and profligate, a young man lives to please only himself. Until one day, with his money gone, his friends gone and himself an outcast he 'comes to his senses' (Luke 15:17). What he does at that point is to decide to go back, to return (re-turn).

He goes, with no expectation of welcome or reinstatement, but only a desire to be once again a member of his father's household. The amazing outcome of his return is, of course, his father's welcome, the complete reinstatement as son, and the celebration feast.

Earlier in the same chapter, Jesus had already explained, twice, the joy that pervades heaven when a sinner repents, when the lost are found, and this story emphasises it again. So we can be absolutely sure of our own welcome when we begin to put the principles of this chapter into action. On the day of your conversion, heaven went wild with joy. And every time you come back and repent, whether it be of major sin, or of wrong attitudes, lack of love or selfishness, there is another party in heaven.

No one says it's going to be easy. The struggle of the butterfly to escape its cocoon (p.141) is a hard one. But read again those three stories in Luke 15 before you embark on this chapter, and listen for the cheering of the angels!

Questions to consider

- '*He found himself in the throes of repentance – the sp revolution that takes place in the soul when one begins to realise one's need to find forgiveness for sin and turn one's life over to God*' (p.139).

  How big a part did repentance play in your own conversion?

- Which of the three stories in Luke 15 do you most identify with: the sheep that has strayed away, the coin that lies hidden and lost, or the rebellious child?

A NEW VIEW

Have you ever been in a room and noticed someone, or a group of people, on the other side? For a moment you observe them, dispassionately, wondering who they are. And then with a sudden shock, you realise that you are looking into a mirror, and what you are seeing is yourself and your own family or friends.

Usually the moment is too short to allow of any detailed observation, but you might have thought fleetingly that the person in the mirror was fat, or old, or dressed in the wrong colour, or looking miserable. But all too quickly the impression fades, and you return to your own inbuilt ideas about who you are and how you look.

James tells us that the Word of God is a mirror (James 1:22–25). It shows us clearly what we are and what we look like in the sight of God. And only those who take action as a result of what they see will be blessed by God.

As Selwyn Hughes takes us through the meaning and importance of repentance, a mirror will be held up to you. Do you want to go on being the person in the mirror, or do you want to do something about it? You might receive a bit of a jolt as you catch sight of yourself in a mirror and think yourself old or fat, but what will happen when you see your soul in the Word of God will be more like an earthquake.

> *'Repentance,' says Dr John White, 'is a changed way of looking at things'* [Changing on the Inside, Eagle Publishing]. *He defines repentance as the shock that comes from seeing reality. It is a terrible thing to claim to be a Christian and yet to live independently of the life offered to us in Christ, to relegate God to irrelevance. The full realisation of that, brought about by the Holy Spirit, can, says John White, be like an earthquake in the soul. Without this inner revolution, this earthquake in the soul, nothing deep and profound happens in a person's spiritual life.* (p.143)

Questions to consider

- *'Suddenly I felt naked and unclean'* (Charles Colson, p.143). Have you ever had an experience like this? What caused it? How did you respond?

• *'Repent and be baptised'* (Acts 2:38). How important do you think the act of baptism is in the process of repentance?

THE WAY TO LIVE

One of the lessons artists and designers have to learn is the law of perspective: things in the distance look smaller. In the theatre, you might 'cheat' the audience into thinking there is a long street on the stage by placing street lamps from the front to the back, tall at the front, and gradually reducing in size to the back of the stage. Et voilà! It looks like a long street.

Perspective is how you see things from where you are standing. If you stand in a different place, then things will look different. So, if you are standing in the wings of the stage, you will see the street lamps as they really are.

This whole question of repentance is also a matter of where you stand. There is an old hymn which includes the words:

Those who fain would serve thee best
Are conscious most of wrong within.

It seems that the nearer we are to God, the more our view of ourselves will change; we can no longer 'cheat' ourselves into thinking that we are anything but weak, needy and quite incapable of pleasing Him.

'*Repentance … is also a daily attitude, a perspective*' (Colson, p.146). As you study this part of Selwyn Hughes' chapter on repentance, be prepared to move to a different place, so that you can see yourself as you really are. And then you need to make sure that you stand in that place every day of your life.

In John 13, Jesus to His disciples, 'A person who has had a bath needs only to wash his feet.' You may indeed have repented fully at your conversion, but daily contact with the world, daily challenges to your love of self, daily attacks from the enemy will mean that you need to have Jesus 'wash your feet'.

Questions to consider

- How would you explain to a new Christian, unfamiliar with Scripture, what it means to 'abide in Christ' (John 15:4–8).

- On pages 147 and 148 Selwyn Hughes describes some of the things that took the place of Christ in his life. What are your 'other lovers'?

....

....

....

....

- *'Repentance [is] … a kind of death'* (p.155). How can we embrace something that is so against our human nature?

....

....

....

....

ACTION PLAN

- Having read through this chapter, is there something you believe you need to repent of? Read through Selwyn Hughes' prayer of repentance on page 149, and then write your own, listing the things that you truly want to turn away from.

- '*Repentance is not regret. Regret is being sorry for oneself ...*
  Repentance is not remorse. Remorse is sorrow without hope at its heart ...
  Repentance is not reformation. Reformation ... may follow repentance, but it can never precede it.
  Repentance is not reparation. Reparation ... is practical proof of the reality of repentance ...' (p.141).
  Spend some time studying these four words and what they mean, and how they differ from true repentance.

- '*We do men and women a disservice when we try to make it easy for them to enter the Christian life*' (p.142). Do you think this is true in your church? What can you do to ensure that the need for repentance is made clear?

- What steps can you take to avoid living in '*a state of nervous tension*' (p.158)?

- Plan into your daily times alone with God a period of confession. Make a 'check list' of the things which you have identified in your study of this chapter, and ask the Holy Spirit to help you turn away from sin daily.

Law 7

Cultivate Your Soul

" *The truth is, of course, that like many things in this world success comes when God and man team up. Though God is the one who designed the soul, it requires care and husbandry on the part of the human being who possesses it, if it is to grow and develop in the way it should. If the worship of God is the first law of the soul, then most certainly the cultivation of it is an important law also. If it isn't cultivated then it will degenerate and die!* " (p.160)

THE CULTIVATION OF THE SOUL

The first thing that Almighty God did after the work of creation, and His day's rest, was to plant a garden. The Creator of the earth was so pleased with His creation that He moved around it, choosing this plant, and that tree, and that shrub. He rejoiced in the beauty and fruitfulness of the earth, celebrating it in a lovely garden.

And down through the ages He has used the lessons of the

vine and the fig tree, the rose and the cedar, the seed and the harvest, to teach His children the lessons of His kingdom.

Selwyn Hughes too, in this final chapter, uses an analogy drawn from the worlds of horticulture and agriculture: and speaks of the necessity of cultivating the soul. Unfortunately, we humans are often content with exactly the way things are, and we have no desire to start clearing the ground, ploughing up the earth and planting what our heavenly Father wishes to grow.

We prefer the crop of blackberries that appears as a result of letting the hedges run wild, and we love the colour of the yellow ragwort that invades the fields. We like to see the bindweed winding its way around every plant in our garden, and we don't realise until too late that the choice we have made leads to degeneration and death.

Any farmer will tell you that the cultivation is hard work. So as you come to this final chapter, you will need to be prepared to buckle down. As someone once said:

> A garden is a lovely thing,
> But gardens are not made
> By saying, 'Oh how beautiful!'
> And sitting in the shade.

Questions to consider

- *When we turn to the Bible and ask ourselves the question, what is the soul? we get the best answers. Although there are many connotations to the word (and Bible writers didn't seem to give precise technical definitions to words like 'heart', 'mind' and 'soul'), the word appears to have two distinct meanings – life and personality* (p.163).

  How much do you think about your soul?

  _____

  _____

  _____

  _____

- *'When [the soul] comes into the kingdom it has the feeling of coming into its own'* (p.164). Did you experience this sense of homecoming and comfort on your conversion?

  _____

  _____

  _____

  _____

THE DISEASE OF THE SOUL

Do you want to know the difference between influenza and a cold? Imagine a £50 note on the lawn outside your house. You look down from your bedroom window and see it. If you decide to go down and pick it up, you only have a cold. If you decide you can't be bothered, not even for £50, then you have the flu!

Sickness of the soul is one that cannot be seen by others, but like the flu it can paralyse us and make any change too great an effort to contemplate. We may be playing our part in an active church, teaching or leading, joining in worship or serving others. But we know that something is wrong. Selwyn Hughes uses the word 'degeneration'.

The law of degeneration runs through the whole of creation. If we neglect our body it will rapidly deteriorate. If it is the mind we neglect then it will degenerate into imbecility. If the conscience, it will run off into lawlessness and vice.
With this law or principle staring us in the face the words of the writer to the Hebrews rise almost to cosmic proportions:

For if the word spoken through angels proved steadfast, and every transgression and disobedience received a just reward, how shall we escape if we neglect so great salvation, which at the first began to be spoken by the Lord, and was confirmed to us by those who heard Him.
Heb. 2:2, NKJV

> *If we neglect the usual means of keeping a garden in order*
> *how shall it escape turning to weeds? If we neglect the soul*
> *how shall it escape dissolution and death?* (p.166).

While others seem to grow in grace and love, we seem to getting further and further behind: '*The power that pulls us down, lowering us, blinding reason, searing conscience, paralysing the will*' (p.168).

And the cause? Simply neglect.

If you think that your soul is degenerating, rather than growing, then now is the time to take action. Resolve to neglect it no longer.

Questions to consider

- '*Experience shows that we will shape ourselves further into sin ... unless we expend some energy and effort to move against it*' (p.166). Has this been your experience? Is there an area of your spiritual life which continues to deteriorate?

- *'The Christian life is a way of living and not merely a decision once made'* (p.168). How different is your 'way of living' from those who are not believers, and who have not made that decision?

THE ANTIDOTE

Often, when we need to understand an abstract concept like the soul, it is the poet who is able to help us the most. By using imagery and words that spark ideas and thoughts in our minds, poets can help us make sense of the unseen world.

In Psalm 1, David paints a picture of those who are blessed by God, those who are cultivating their souls. He tells us that they are like trees planted by the water's edge. Of course, any analogy breaks down at some point: in this case, a tree cannot actually decide where to plant itself. But, as Selwyn Hughes explains in this final section of his book, we can so decide. We can decide that we *will* spend time with God; we *will* read His Word regularly; we *will* learn how to listen to Him and pray to Him.

For years now, a conviction has been growing in my heart that the Christian life rises and falls at the point of the devotional – those times when one meets privately with the Lord to deepen one's intimacy with Him. There the soul becomes at its best (p. 172).

The quiet time … shuts you in with God, the door closes upon you and then infinite resources begin to bubble up from beneath and you are lifted up. The door opens and you glide out onto a higher level of life. You will be surprised – and other people will too – at how easily you transcend worries and fears and difficulties and seem to live life on a higher level. It's the result of being shut in with God.

That's the power of the quiet time – the place where the soul grows best. (p.182)

As we saw earlier, the work of cultivation is hard work, but the river of the life of God is available for us to draw on. The Holy Spirit is ready and waiting to lead us into all truth. And we have His promise that, if we do undertake this work of cultivation, *'whatever we do will prosper'* (Psa. 1:3).

ACTION PLAN

* *'The nurse of full-grown souls is solitude'* (James Russell Lowell, p.171).
  How often are you able to be alone with God? Plan to

increase the amount of time, and to give that time priority in your day.

- *'Read your Bible'* (p.176).
  Can you think of three ways in which you could increase the quantity and quality of your Bible reading?

- *'Listen to God'* (p.178).
  Resolve to buy and read the book quoted on page 179, and to give time to learning how to listen for the voice of God.

- *'Pray'* (p.180).
  Start a notebook in which to record specific prayers (and their answers!).

- *'Salvation in its broadest sense is salvation from the downward bias of the soul. It takes in the whole process of rescue from the power of sin and selfishness that goes on all the time in our lives, the power that pulls us down, lowering us, blinding reason, searing conscience, paralysing the will.'* (p.167).
  What steps can your church take to ensure that new Christians are taught how to enter fully into salvation, and how to 'cultivate their souls'?

Congratulations on finishing this workbook. Come back to it on occasions and we promise you that you will discover, with the Holy Spirit's help, new insights and new understanding.

Notes

Notes

Notes

Notes

Notes

National Distributors

UK: (and countries not listed below)
CWR, Waverley Abbey House, Waverley Lane, Farnham, Surrey GU9 8EP.
Tel: (01252) 784710 Outside UK (44) 1252 784710

AUSTRALIA: CMC Australasia, PO Box 519, Belmont, Victoria 3216.
Tel: (03) 5241 3288

CANADA: Cook Communications Ministries, PO Box 98, 55 Woodslee Avenue, Paris,
Ontario. Tel: 1800 263 2664

GHANA: Challenge Enterprises of Ghana, PO Box 5723, Accra.
Tel: (021) 222437/223249 Fax: (021) 226227

HONG KONG: Cross Communications Ltd, 1/F, 562A Nathan Road, Kowloon.
Tel: 2780 1188 Fax: 2770 6229

INDIA: Crystal Communications, 10-3-18/4/1, East Marredpally, Secunderabad – 500 026.
Tel/Fax: (040) 7732801

KENYA: Keswick Books and Gifts Ltd, PO Box 10242, Nairobi.
Tel: (02) 331692/226047 Fax: (02) 728557

MALAYSIA: Salvation Book Centre (M) Sdn Bhd, 23 Jalan SS 2/64,
47300 Petaling Jaya, Selangor.
Tel: (03) 78766411/78766797 Fax: (03) 78757066/78756360

NEW ZEALAND: CMC Australasia, PO Box 36015, Lower Hutt.
Tel: 0800 449 408 Fax: 0800 449 049

NIGERIA: FBFM, Helen Baugh House, 96 St Finbarr's College Road, Akoka, Lagos.
Tel: (01) 7747429/4700218/825775/827264

PHILIPPINES: OMF Literature Inc, 776 Boni Avenue, Mandaluyong City.
Tel: (02) 531 2183 Fax: (02) 531 1960

REPUBLIC OF IRELAND: Scripture Union, 40 Talbot Street, Dublin 1.
Tel: (01) 8363764

SINGAPORE: Armour Publishing Pte Ltd, Block 203A Henderson Road,
11–06 Henderson Industrial Park, Singapore 159546.
Tel: 6 276 9976 Fax: 6 276 7564

SOUTH AFRICA: Struik Christian Books, 80 MacKenzie Street, PO Box 1144,
Cape Town 8000. Tel: (021) 462 4360 Fax: (021) 461 3612

SRI LANKA: Christombu Books, 27 Hospital Street, Colombo 1.
Tel: (01) 433142/328909

TANZANIA: CLC Christian Book Centre, PO Box 1384, Mkwepu Street, Dar es Salaam.
Tel/Fax (022) 2119439

USA: Cook Communications Ministries, PO Box 98, 55 Woodslee Avenue, Paris,
Ontario, Canada. Tel: 1800 263 2664

ZIMBABWE: Word of Life Books, Shop 4, Memorial Building,
35 S Machel Avenue, Harare. Tel: (04) 781305 Fax: (04) 774739

For email addresses, visit the CWR website: www.cwr.org.uk

CWR is a registered charity – number 294387

Trusted
All Over the World

Daily Devotionals

Books and Videos

Day and Residential Courses

Counselling Training

Biblical Study Courses

Regional Seminars

Ministry to Women

CWR have been providing training and resources for Christians since the 1960s. From our headquarters at Waverley Abbey House we have been serving God's people with a vision to help apply God's Word to everyday life and relationships. The daily devotional *Every Day with Jesus* is read by over three-quarters of a million people in more than 150 countries, and our unique courses in biblical studies and pastoral care are respected all over the world.

For a free brochure about our seminars and courses or a catalogue of CWR resources please contact us at the following address:

CWR,
Waverley Abbey House,
Waverley Lane,
Farnham,
Surrey GU9 8EP
UK

Telephone: 01252 784700
Email: mail@cwr.org.uk
Website: www.cwr.org.uk

 CRUSADE FOR WORLD REVIVAL   *Applying God's Word to everyday life and relationships*

Christ Empowered Living – New Format

Christ Empowered Living is Selwyn Hughes' dynamic core teaching in one easy to digest volume.

It will transform your life with essential principles of Christian living and develop you to your full spiritual potential. You will discover biblical insights that will revolutionise your approach to the way you live and help to renew your mind.
This new edition improves readability and gives larger margins for notes.

Softback, 312 pages ISBN: 1-85345-201-7

£7.99

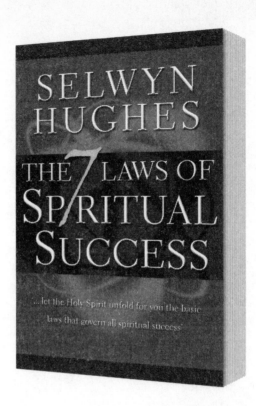

The 7 Laws of Spiritual Success

Just as there are laws in nature that hold our physical world together, so there are laws for life that make our spiritual walk a success. This book is Selwyn Hughes' legacy to future generations and essential reading for anyone who has been inspired by his teaching and ability to apply God's Word to everyday life and relationships.

* The primacy of worship   * Making gratitude a habit
* Never give up   * The art of forgiveness
* The law of service   * Daily repentance
* Growth and development

Softback, 208 pages ISBN: 1-85345-237-8

£7.99